About the Books

Writers and Readers Documentary Comic Books are Introductions to some of the major thinkers and ideas of our time. Their form pioneers an attempt to bring words and images together and to translate the most complicated information into a simple, readable and amusing story. They challenge accepted educational notions, presenting simplifications that are intelligent and not patronizing.

Originally intended for the uninitiated, experts from all over the world have come to admire and use the series.

We began the series with books on Marx, Einstein and Freud. These provided the stepping stones for future books in history, current events, philosophy, psychology and the biological and physical sciences. New lines of development are continuing.

While the Beginners Series was originally published in England, it is today available in sixteen languages and in many of the world's major cities, from Tokyo to New York.

OTHER BOOKS IN THIS SERIES:

Cuba For Beginners
Marx For Beginners
Lenin For Beginners
Nuclear Power For Beginners
Freud For Beginners
Einstein For Beginners
Mao For Beginners
Trotsky For Beginners
Capitalism For Beginners
Ecology For Beginners
Das Kapital For Beginners

Economists For Beginners
Darwin For Beginners
Food For Beginners
French Revolution For Beginners
Ireland For Beginners
DNA For Beginners
Peace For Beginners
Medicine For Beginners
Orwell For Beginners
Reagan For Beginners

FORTHCOMING BOOKS:

Black History For Beginners
The Brain For Beginners
Computers For Beginners
Reich For Beginners
Socialism For Beginners

Anarchy For Beginners
Feminism For Beginners
Architecture For Beginners
Sex For Beginners
Newton For Beginners

© **WRITERS AND READERS Documentary Comic Books**

NICARAGUA
FOR BEGINNERS

BY RIUS

WRITERS AND READERS PUBLISHING, INCORPORATED
One West 125th Street
Dr. Martin Luther King, Jr. Blvd.
New York, N.Y. 10027

A Writers and Readers Documentary Comic Book
Copyright © 1984
ISBN 0 86316 069 7
3 4 5 6 7 8 9 0
Manufactured in the United States of America
Beginners Documentary Comic books are published by
Writers and Readers Publishing, Inc. Its trademark, con-
sisting of the words "For Beginners, Writers and Readers
Documentary Comic Books" and the portrayal of a seal
bearing the words "Beginners Documentary Comic
Books" and Writers and Readers logo, is registered in the
U.S. Patent and Trademark Office and in other countries.

Chapter 1:

French map made in 1650 showing the political divisions of Mexico, Guadalajara, and Guatemala, which included Chiapas and Central America.

About two thousand years ago (more or less), a lot of Indians came to Nicaragua, mostly from Mexico, some from the Caribbean.

The newly arrived tourists and exiles decided to settle there since they liked the many rivers and lagoons and the abundance of good land, as well as the lush green countryside.

AND VOLCANOS! THERE'S ONE FOR EACH TRIBE.

The first inhabitants of Nicaragua were probably the Mosquitos (not the kind that bite), who were later pushed out by the Chorotegas, who were in turn pushed aside by the Nahuas from Mexico. They imposed their Mexican culture on the region.

IN OTHER WORDS, WE NICARAGUANS ARE HALF MEXICAN.

The number of place names which sound like Mexican ones, as well as the Mexican-looking faces, are proof of Nicaragua's Mexican heritage.

Iztapalapa, Amecameca, Jalapa, Ajusco, Amatitlán, Tonalá, Chapultepec, Comalcalco, Olinalá, Cuajimcuilapa, Panzacola, etc.

And the corn-based diet is almost like Mexican food.

They knew math, a little astronomy, the decimal system (with base five), and, like the Mexicans, they farmed, hunted, and fished.

But it's hot as hell!

They lived in relative peace and prosperity, eating off gold plates. Then one day, as was the custom in those times, they were

DISCOVERED.

This great deed was acomplished by

Admiral Christopher Columbus,

who made his living discovering.

The Date?

September 12, 1502.

The Place?

the mouth of the Rama River, at the site of the present town of Bluefields on the Atlantic Coast.

"Nicaragua has the best land and people that we've found in the New World. There's high ground, many rivers and lots of tall trees."

So...

after 15 days of collecting gold, parrots, and women, Columbus and his prospectors brought the news back to Spain.

Nothing has been the same since.

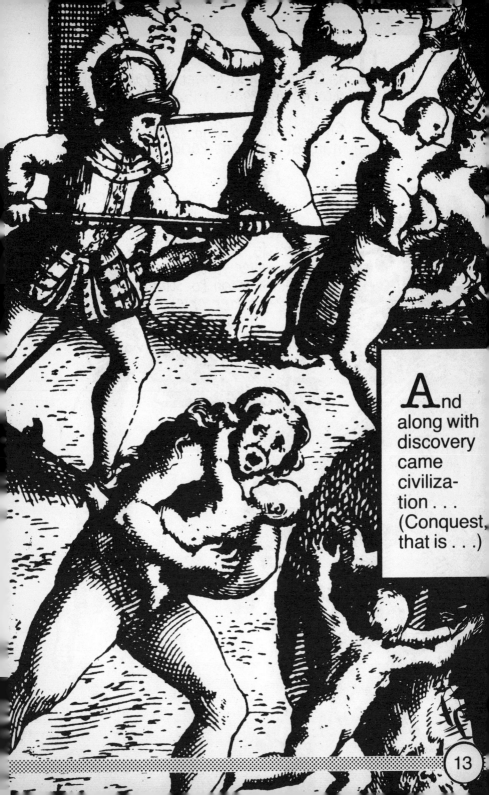

And along with discovery came civiliza-tion . . . (Conquest, that is . . .)

13

The Conquest and Christianization of Nicaragua began in 1523, when two cruel, ambitious conquistadores, Gil Gonzáles Dávila and Andrés Niño, marched up from Panama.

The Nicaraguan chiefs Nicoya and Nicaragua were taken peacefully (in other words, they were tricked). However, it took armed persuasion to subdue the other chief, Diriangén.

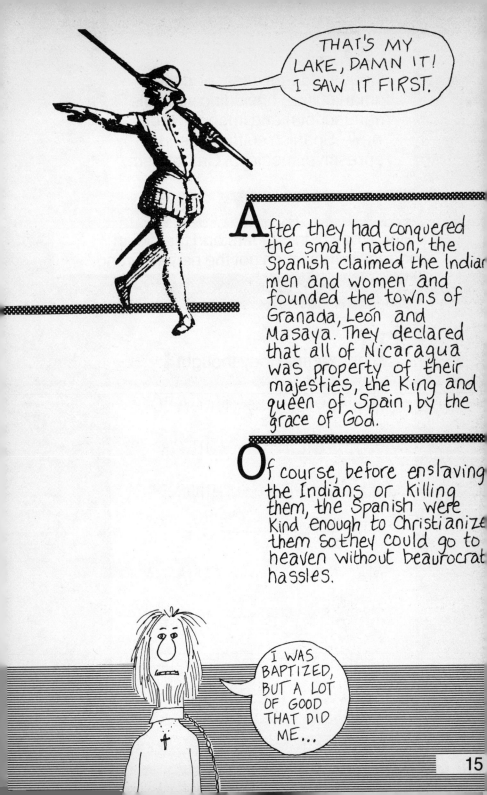

THAT'S MY LAKE, DAMN IT! I SAW IT FIRST.

After they had conquered the small nation, the Spanish claimed the Indian men and women and founded the towns of Granada, León and Masaya. They declared that all of Nicaragua was property of their majesties, the King and queen of Spain, by the grace of God.

Of course, before enslaving the Indians or killing them, the Spanish were kind enough to Christianize them so they could go to heaven without beaurocrat hassles.

I WAS BAPTIZED, BUT A LOT OF GOOD THAT DID ME...

15

Just as in Mexico, the conquistadores destroyed the Indian culture (including valuable manuscripts) and imposed their "new" Spanish culture based on repressive, medieval Catholicism.

Since they didn't understand the Indian languages, they even got the names wrong.

For example they thought :

NAHUALOTLI was NAGAROTE

XILOATL ⟶ JILOA

CHINAMCALTECA ⟶ CHINANDEGA

ITZTETLI ⟶ ESTELÍ

MANAHUAC ⟶ MANAGUA

MASALTYAN ⟶ MASAYA

CHIPOATLI ⟶ CHIPOTE

CIHUACOATL ⟶ SÉBACO

MATLALCAPAN ⟶ MATAGALPA...

It soon became apparent that there were Nicaraguans of various classes and colors.

1ST **CLASS:**
Whites born in Spain.

2ND **CLASS:**
Whites born in Nicaragua.

3RD **CLASS:**
Mestizos (children of Spaniards and Nicaraguans).

4TH **CLASS:**
Dark-skinned Indians. Blacks on the Atlantic Coast.

Wait a minute! Where did those blacks come from?

They're slaves who fled the West Indies and settled on the Atlantic Coast.

The Atlantic Coast, isolated from the rest of the country, was conquered by the British. In **1625**, they established the PROTECTORATE of MESQUITIA, full of blacks, Rama, Sumo and Mosquito Indians (now called Miskitos).

As in the rest of Spanish America, Nicaraguans got tired of supporting the Spanish and declared

INDEPENDENCE

So in **1821** Mexico and Central America became independent of the mother country.

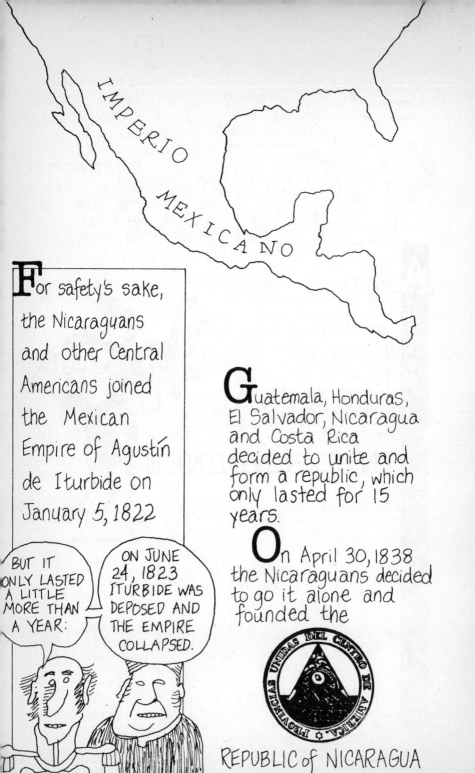

IMPERIO MEXICANO

For safety's sake, the Nicaraguans and other Central Americans joined the Mexican Empire of Agustín de Iturbide on January 5, 1822

BUT IT ONLY LASTED A LITTLE MORE THAN A YEAR:

ON JUNE 24, 1823 ITURBIDE WAS DEPOSED AND THE EMPIRE COLLAPSED.

Guatemala, Honduras, El Salvador, Nicaragua and Costa Rica decided to unite and form a republic, which only lasted for 15 years.

On April 30, 1838 the Nicaraguans decided to go it alone and founded the

PROVINCIAS UNIDAS DEL CENTRO DE AMÉRICA

REPUBLIC of NICARAGUA

In the years after Independence the country was practically in anarchy, torn by hatred, local rivalries, disputes, and rebellions.

21

The first Nicaraguan leaders emerged from the power struggles between the best families of León and Granada.

Thus in 1855 Señor Castellón hired Mr. Byron Cole to supply 200 mercenaries while Señor Jerez hired 500 filibusters from Mr. Fisher.

As we'll see . . .

Taking advantage of Mexico's weakness, the Americans stole half of its territory...

1847

Since it was so easy to grab California, New Mexico, Arizona, Texas, Nevada, and Utah, the U.S. decided to pick up some more bargains, starting with Baja, California.

23

An adventurer named WILLIAM WALKER

was sent to invade this strategic peninsula.

This pressured Mexico into selling the U.S.

THE GASDEN PURCHASE

Only later was it learned that the real reason for Walker's invasion was to pressure Mexico into selling the Gasden purchase.

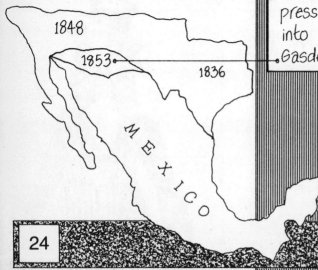

1848

1853

1836

MEXICO

Since the Gasden affair was so successful, Walker was sent to Nicaragua, the most promising route for an interoceanic canal.

Shortly before Walker's arrival, an American millionaire, Cornelius Vanderbilt, obtained concessions to build a canal across Nicaragua and to establish an interoceanic passenger route.

From 1851 to 1856 Vanderbilt's company took 100,000 people across Nicaragua. When Walker arrived, he decided to replace Vanderbilt and become lord and master of Nicaragua.

25

Walker assumed Mr. Cole's
contract to supply mercenaries
to Señor Castellón, and in
June 1855 he arrived with
his "volunteers."
A year passed, then Walker
proclaimed himself President
of Nicaragua.

WILLIAM WALKER
"Grey-eyed Man of Destiny"

Born May 8, 1824. Walker moved to
this site from 6th Ave. N. in 1840
In early life he was doctor, lawyer
& journalist. He invaded Mexico in
1853 with 46 men & proclaimed himself Pres., Republic of Lower Calif.
Led force into Nicaragua in 1855;
was elected its Pres. in 1856. In
attempt to wage war on Honduras was
captured & executed Sept. 12 1860.

Historical marker in
Nashville, Tennessee

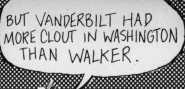

So the U.S. withdrew its support from Walker, who was already under pressure from the British who wanted the Canal route too.

And so England armed the Costa Ricans, after convincing them that Walker was dangerous. Costa Rica defeated the American pirate and the U.S. withdrew (temporarily) from Nicaragua: **1857.**

BUT WALKER COULDN'T TAKE A HINT AND CAME BACK.

He suddenly showed up in November 1857, and seized the port of San Juan del Norte. Two months later the British ran him off.

He came back again in 1860, this time to Honduras. There he was captured by the British and finally shot...

SOME HISTORIANS SAY HE WAS HANGED. SAME DIFFERENCE.

While England was meddling in Nicaragua, the U.S. had to stay on the sidelines.

Surprisingly enough it was a postage stamp which saved Nicaragua from having a Canal Zone.

In 1902 each US senator received a copy of this 1899 Nicaraguan stamp.

The stamp showed a typically Nicaraguan landscape.

But we're jumping ahead...
You might ask what happened in Nicaragua between 1850 and 1900 ...

Nicaragua was stuck with a long string of aristocrats who took land from Indians and gave it to coffee planters and American investors.

Aristocrats from the city of Granada "governed" for over 50 years, keeping "order" and helping the rich get richer. The poor accepted their fate -- being poor and exploited.

TO GET TO HEAVEN ALL YOU NEED IS A LITTLE . . .

The presidency was only for those with the right surnames. The same families followed each other through the presidency. Even though they could barely read and write, these presidents could certainly sign treaties giving the country's wealth to foreigners who were even richer than they were.

WE'LL HAVE TO WHITEWASH THE PLACE. WE'VE GOT TOO MANY INDIANS...

31

The financial, military and religious oligarchies saw the U.S. as the model to follow, even though their only exposure to it was shopping trips to New Orleans and Miami.

CAPITALISM

A system in which, as its name implies, the only thing which matters is capital.

Granada's oligarchy was still living in the 18th century.

WE SHOULD RE-ESTABLISH SLAVERY!

It failed to understand the liberal reforms enacted in the United States to enable it to become a modern, productive nation.

The oligarchy did virtually re-establish slavery—— it took the Indians' rich, communally-owned lands...

More than 7000 people died in the war which broke out in 1881 when the aristocracy took the Indians' communal lands for coffee plantations and lumbering.

THEY DON'T WANT TO DEVELOP IT, SO WE'LL DO IT FOR THEM.

33

Since the United States didn't have a Canal Zone in Nicaragua, the United Fruit Company created a banana zone in Nicaragua, and began exploiting peasants and exporting coffee, bananas, and other fruit.

Working as a team, U.S. capitalists and local aristocrats made the original land-owners serfs on huge plantations.

They worked there for a pittance their entire lives, making the rich richer and giving birth to Nicaraguan capitalism.

I LIKE NICARAGUA

Cathedral of San Pedro, León

The oligarchy in the city of León was a little more progressive than its counterpart in Granada (they crossed themselves, but with the left hand). They took power in 1893 under the leadership of General José Santos Zelaya.

THE DEVIL!

Zelaya admired Mexican President Juaréz, and using his presidency as a model, he carried out reforms, which for a country as conservative as Nicaragua, was a real revolution.

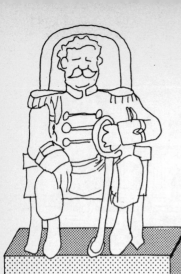

Zelaya, God forbid, separated church and state, limited the power and wealth of the church, promulgated a liberal constitution, challenged the power of the landed elite, and reformed the judiciary.

AND CANCELLED U.S. CONCESSIONS!

HE SCREWED HIMSELF!

So Uncle Sam, infuriated by Zelaya's hostile actions (reasserting control of the Atlantic Coast, taxing U.S. investors, promoting a canal, etc.), decided to oust Zelaya. The U.S. backed a conservative "revolution" to eliminate the "dictator."

GERMANY WANTS A SATELLITE IN THE AMERICAS!*

* International Communism hadn't been invented yet.

AND SO:

armed and backed by the U.S., two conservative generals, Estrada and Chamorro, rebelled against Zelaya, who comitted the error of shooting a pair of American spies, who had tried to blow up two Nicaraguan ships.

The United States, whose ships were already off the Nicaraguan coast, broke relations with Zelaya and DEMANDED his resignation.

THIS IS MUCHO BAD, I'M MUCHO MAD!

"... President of the United States no longer has confidence in and respect for President Zelaya. I am enclosing your passport in case you want to leave the country."
   -Philander Knox, Secretary of state

Needless to say, Zelaya had to resign. On Christmas Day, 1909, a Mexican boat rescued him from Nicaragua, much to Uncle Sam's displeasure.

When Zelaya resigned, the Nicaraguan Congress named another liberal, José Madriz, as president.

BUT THE GRINGOS DIDN'T LIKE HIM EITHER.

HE NOT ONLY ATTACKED THEM, BUT DECISIVELY DEFEATED THEM!

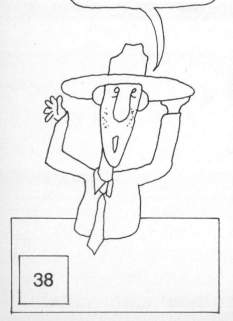

Knox declared he would not accept Madriz as president.

However, Madriz didn't pay any attention to him and attacked the conservative rebels.

... to prevent the defeat of his beloved conservatives, Uncle Sam told Madriz that if he as much as touched the U.S. boats delivering arms to the conservatives, he would have to fight the U.S.

Madriz thus resigned on August 20, 1910 and the United States imposed a quadrumvirate (or however you spell it).

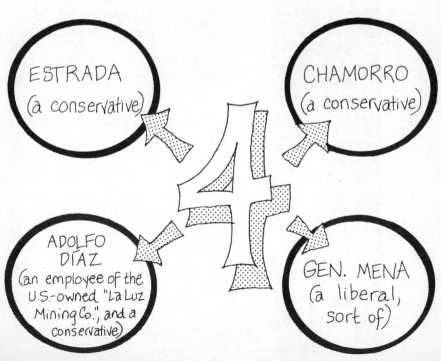

ESTRADA (a conservative)

CHAMORRO (a conservative)

ADOLFO DÍAZ (an employee of the U.S.-owned "La Luz Mining Co.", and a conservative)

GEN. MENA (a liberal, sort of)

However, the real governors were Messieurs Weitzel and Dawson, who drafted legislation, signed reparation treaties, and issued economic directives. It was so disgusting that Estrada resigned, leaving Mr. Díaz in power.

THUS
an obscure book-keeper became President of Nicaragua.

Within a few months he had mortgaged the country, and ceded the ports, customs revenues, railroads, and banks to the U.S. Finally even the conservative congress couldn't take it, so it named Gen. Mena as president. Not suprisingly the Americans didn't like him. When he tried to take power, he was defeated by U.S. troops supporting Gen. Chamorro, and had to flee the country.

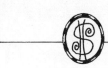

WHO?

Benjamín Zeledón, a doctor, teacher, and aide to General Mena, decided to stay in Nicaragua and fight the Americans and their puppet, Díaz, who immediately asked for U.S. troops saying:

The grave dangers which threaten us can only be withstood by means of prompt U.S. aid, which was so effective in Cuba.

Thus <u>to save democracy</u>, the heroic U.S. Marines landed August 4, 1912 at the request of the traitor Díaz.

2

Zeledón entrenched
his poorly armed
forces in Masaya,
where U.S. artillery
bombed them
for a day.
Zeledón was then
captured and shot.
The rest of
his force (more
than 300 men) had
their throats
cut or were shot.

Nicaragua
would remain
under American
occupation
from 1912
until 1933.

WHEN
SANDINO RAN
US OFF

hic!

In fact they
were driven
out by some-
one who as
a boy saw
the body of
Benjamín Zeledón
being taken
to the
cemetery:

AUGUSTO
CÉZAR SANDINO.

Chapter 2:

Sandino, the Father

Augusto César Sandino was born May 19, 1895 in an Indian village named Niquinohomo.

MANAGUA
☀ · NIQUINOHOMO

Gregorio Sandino, his father, owned some land, and his mother, Margarita Calderón, was a peasant of Indian ancestry.

Augusto César* (this name reflects the Nicaraguan custom of giving children "different" names) attended primary school and studied some bookkeeping, since his father wanted him to administer his coffee plantations and other farms.

* Sandino's __real__ name was Augusto Nicolás, according to his birth certificate.

NOR RICH, JUST HALF & HALF

SO HE WASN'T POOR?

Birth certificate:
Sandino signed
his name
Augusto C. Sandino.
The "C" was
for Calderón.
Thus the confusion,
having one name
and being called
something else.

I n 1921 Sandino fled after wounding Dagoberto Rivas in a political dispute.

DAGOBERTO LATER BECAME MAYOR, SO SANDINO COULDN'T COME BACK

F rom 1921 to 1925 Sandino worked in Honduras and Guatemala for the United Fruit Company, and then in Mexico he worked for the South Penn. Oil Company.
   Later he was head of the gasoline sales department of the Huasteca Petroleum Company, also in Mexico.

YOU MEAN HE BECAME POLITIZED IN MEXICO?

SURE, HE WAS A WORKER THERE!

S trangely enough, working for the Americans, Sandino became aware of what imperialism was. At this time trade unions began struggling against the U.S. firms that owned Mexico's oil.

"**A**bout 1925 I decided everything in Nicaragua had gone sour and that honor had disappeared. At the same time my sincerity attracted a group of like-minded friends. Each day we would comment on the submission of our people before the advance, by treachery or force, of Yankee imperialism.

On one such day I said to my friends, if there were 100 honorable men who loved their country as I did, the absolute sovereignty of our country would be restored."

On May 16, 1926 Sandino quit his job, took the $3000 he had saved, and left for Nicaragua in search of 100 men who thought the way he did.

"ONLY BULLETS WILL MAKE NICARAGUA FREE"

49

Sandino's first recruits were 29 exploited miners in San Albino. He bought his first guns and began "his" war against the United States.

HEY CHIEF! SACASA JUST GOT 700 TONS OF GUNS.

Sacasa was vice-president of Nicaragua. However the conservatives wouldn't let him "vice-govern." Sandino went to him for guns and he told Sandino to go to General Moncada, the army chief-of-staff.

GO JUMP IN THE LAKE, SANDINO

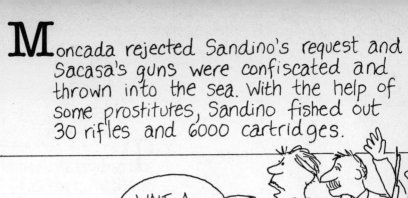

Moncada rejected Sandino's request and Sacasa's guns were confiscated and thrown into the sea. With the help of some prostitutes, Sandino fished out 30 rifles and 6000 cartridges.

WAIT A MINUTE, WE'RE COMING TOO, GENERAL

When they saw that Moncada was siding with the invaders, 200 soldiers joined Sandino, ready to fight by his side to get rid of the American troops.

WAIT A MINUTE. I DON'T UNDERSTAND WHO MONCADA WAS AND WHAT HE WANTED.

WHY DID HE SIDE WITH THE GRINGOS?

READ ON AND YOU'LL FIND OUT ABOUT THE TREASON OF ESPINO NEGRO...

51

1926

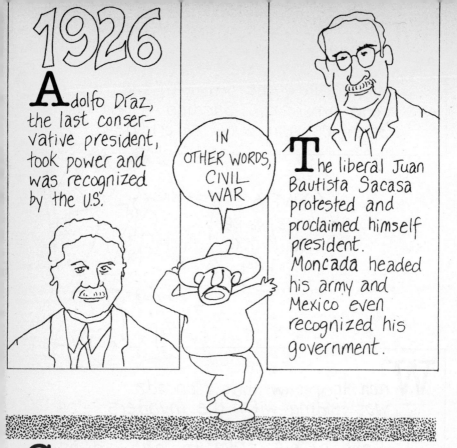

Adolfo Díaz, the last conservative president, took power and was recognized by the U.S.

IN OTHER WORDS, CIVIL WAR

The liberal Juan Bautista Sacasa protested and proclaimed himself president. Moncada headed his army and Mexico even recognized his government.

Sandino joined the liberals and fought with Moncada. They almost beat the conservatives. <u>But</u> when they were about to take Managua, the U.S. cavalry arrived.

PEACE, PEACE, PEACE.

$\mathbf{A}$t the town of Tipitapa the U.S. ambassador convened a "peace" conference in the shade of an espino negro (black thorn) tree.

$\mathbf{T}$here Moncada betrayed Sacasa and agreed to lay down his arms, thus letting Díaz stay on as president until his term was over in 1928.
   Then there were to be elections in which Moncada would be the liberal candidate.

MONCADA'S PLATE OF LENTILS COST UNCLE SAM A MILLION AND A HALF DOLLARS.

$\mathbf{A}$s U.S. Ambassador Stimson's translator we find a "friendly young liberal, frank and agreeable" named ANASTASIO SOMOZA GARCÍA. The peace treaty provided for a national guard, organized separately from the army to protect the president and his government from abuses by the army. The guard was to be trained, led and armed by the Americans.

This betrayal started Sandino thinking:

"I knew that Moncada had betrayed the interests of the revolution and I also bitterly resented the betrayal of the ideals of the Nicaraguan people. I couldn't remain indifferent to the traitor's actions. I remembered at this time how they made fun of Nicaraguans in the rest of the world. I spent three days in the Sierra del Común, sad and depressed. I didn't know whether to surrender my arms or defend my country, which was in such need of love from its people. I broke this chain of thought and decided to fight, feeling I had been called on to protest the betrayal of Nicaragua and its ideals. My bullets would be the only ones which would defend Nicaraguan sovereignty. There was no reason for the United States to interfere in our family affairs. That was when I published my first manifesto."

Thus Sandino refused to lay down his arms.

Moncada preferred not to attack Sandino in the heart of the mountains, so Sandino could spend time organizing and training his men. Before going into combat he got married.

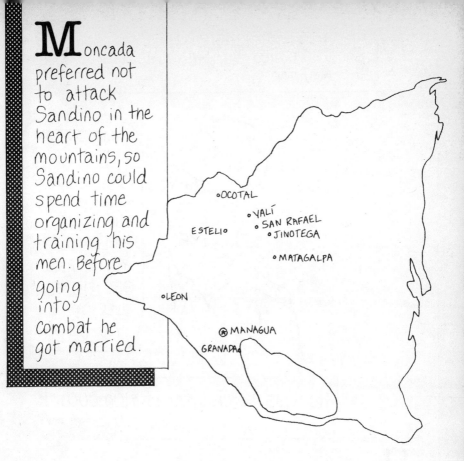

OCOTAL
YALÍ
SAN RAFAEL
ESTELI
JINOTEGA
MATAGALPA
LEON
MANAGUA
GRANADA

On the 28th of May, 1927, between bursts of machine-gun fire, Sandino took as his wife Blanca Arauz, the telegraph operator of San Rafael. She became active in her husband's struggle.

Moncada called Sandino and tried to convince him.

COME ON, SANDINO, YOU CAN RUN JINOTEGA AND KEEP ALL THE MULES YOU HAVE STOLEN. YOU'LL ALSO GET $10 FOR EVERY DAY YOU FOUGHT.

He was later offered $100,000.

Sandino rejected the traitor's offer and withdrew to Jinotega with his 300-man force.

"I'D PREFER TO DIE WITH THE HANDFUL OF MEN WHO CAME WITH ME. IT'S BETTER TO DIE A REBEL THAN TO LIVE AS A SLAVE."

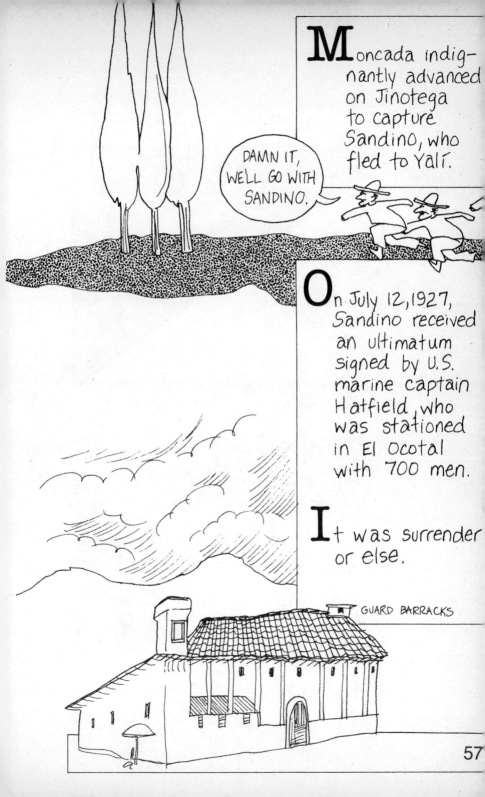

Moncada indignantly advanced on Jinotega to capture Sandino, who fled to Yalí.

DAMN IT, WE'LL GO WITH SANDINO.

On July 12, 1927, Sandino received an ultimatum signed by U.S. marine captain Hatfield, who was stationed in El Ocotal with 700 men.

It was surrender or else.

GUARD BARRACKS

Sandino answered the fair marine captain:

Chipote Camp
(near San Fernando)
TO Captain G.D. Hatfield
El Ocotal

I received your message yesterday and read it. I will not surrender and I await you here. Patria libre o morir.* I am not afraid of you. The patriotism of those who accompany me is my strength.

A.C. Sandino

A free country or death.

58

Instead of waiting for the Americans, Sandino decided to attack them in their lair. He rounded up and armed all the peasants he could find. With this new force of 800 he captured the entire town of Ocotal, except for the barracks.

THERE 40 GRINGOS AND 70 GUARDS-MEN WERE ENTRENCHED.

As they were attacking the barracks, something Sandino and the peasants hadn't thought of appeared:

U.S. AIR POWER

The planes bombed the town and machine-gunned innocent peasants, killing at least 300, including women and children. Sandino was forced to withdraw. President Coolidge later entertained and decorated the pilots, praising their "heroic military action."

After the defeat at El Ocotal, Sandino was defeated again at San Fernando. On the 27th he suffered still another defeat at Las Flores, losing almost all his arms and 70 men... a disaster!

THINGS GOT TOUGH!

"We are alone. Nicaragua's cause has been forgotten. From now on our enemy won't be the forces of the tyrant Díaz, but the marines of the most powerful empire in history. We will fight against them. We will be ruthlessly killed by bombs dropped from the air, stabbed by foreign bayonets, and shot by modern machine-guns." *Nicaragua will triumph

NICARAGUA*
VENCERA

Sandino learned quickly and withdrew to El Chipote, where he built his forces and tried another type of warfare, which would be more favorable to him and the peasants.

GUERRILLA WARFARE! HOT DAMN!

The jungle and the people of the Segovias in northern Nicaragua protected Sandino, who decimated the invaders with guerrilla tactics.

DESPITE THE BISHOP OF GRANADA'S BLESSING THE GRINGOS' GUNS

The holy mother church's sympathies were not with the guerrillas, but with the American invaders and their National Guard collaborators. In fact Sandino and his peasant guerrillas struggled not only against U.S. troops, but against the entire Nicaraguan government and the three pillars which upheld it: the church, the army and the oligarchy.

AND
AINST
ERIALIST
PAGANDA!

Since by this time the world press was controlled by the U.S., it called the Sandinistas "cruel assassins, pillagers, adventurers and rapists with dark instincts, drunken, bloodthirsty agressors, enemies of peace, order and democracy."

IT'S GOOD I NEVER LEARNED TO READ.

And just as they did with Pancho Villa and Emiliano Zapata, they portrayed Sandino as an illiterate, psychopathic killer whose death would be a blessing for Nicaragua. You can read the Mexican press from 1910 to 1917 to see how similar the reporting was.

Sandino went to Mexico to ask for arms and aid but Mexican president Portes Gil, at the request of U.S. ambassador Morrow, refused to let him come any further than Mérida, Yucatán.
Sandino returned, disillusioned with the Mexican "revolutionaries."

WHAT CAN YOU EXPECT FROM THE PEOPLE WHO KILLED ZAPATA?

(Mexico only made up for this in 1978)

What you won't find in the press at the time are detailed accounts of crimes committed by the Americans, the terror imposed on the civilian population to stop them from supporting Sandino.

In 1930 the Americans did to Nicaragua what they were to do in Vietnam in 1970.

o towns leveled

o relocation camps

o indiscriminate bombing

o mass executions

o rape and pillage

(The American Way of Death)

They left Nicaragua just as they left Vietnam, with their tail between their legs. They were unable to beat Sandino and his ragged guerrillas.

On January 1, 1933, U.S. occupation forces left Nicaragua.

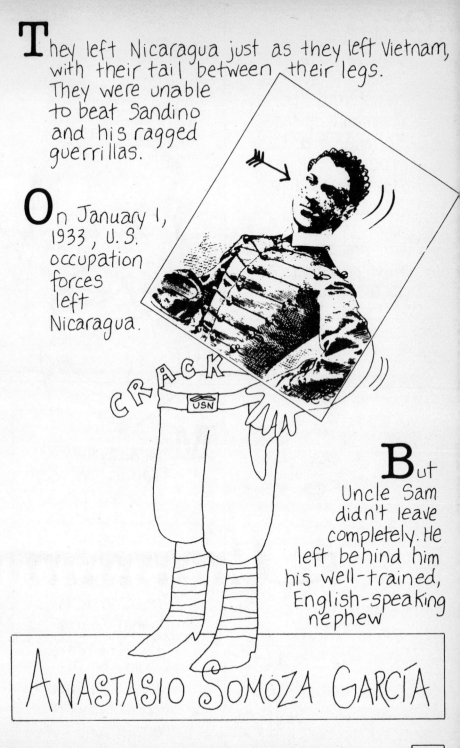

CRACK

USN

But Uncle Sam didn't leave completely. He left behind him his well-trained, English-speaking nephew

ANASTASIO SOMOZA GARCÍA

On the first of January, 1933, General Matthews transferred the command of the National Guard from himself to Major Anastasio Somoza, the lover of the U.S. ambassador's wife, pro-American to his heart.

Moncada, the traitor, had been replaced by Sacasa. After the Americans had left, President Sacasa asked Sandino to lay down his arms so the country would be at peace. Sandino accepted with certain conditions and guarantees.

On February 2, 1933, Sacasa and Sandino signed a peace treaty which recognized Sandino's patriotic actions, stopped the fighting and promised land for Sandino's men.

They embraced as a sign of peace, an embrace which included the real ruler of Nicaragua, National Guard Chief Anastasio Somoza.

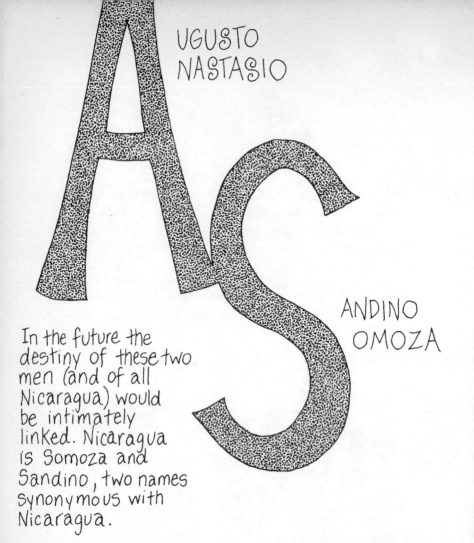

A UGUSTO NASTASIO

AS ANDINO OMOZA

In the future the destiny of these two men (and of all Nicaragua) would be intimately linked. Nicaragua is Somoza and Sandino, two names synonymous with Nicaragua.

NOW FOR A WHILE (OVER FORTY YEARS) WE'LL SEE A LOT OF THE NAME SOMOZA...

¡◎✱◉¨∶◦✕◦! ✗◎✱!✿@!

Chapter 3:

for the Nicaraguans, the biggest son-of-a...

The Somoza Era

Anastasio Somoza García was born in San Marcos, a town near Niquinohomo, in 1896. His family was well off.

AND TO MOVE UP THE SOCIAL LADDER, HE MARRIED SALVADORA DEBAYLE SACASA, THE NIECE OF PRESIDENT SACASA.

Who himself was the son of another Nicaraguan President, Roberto Sacasa.

"AND TO MOVE FURTHER UP THE SOCIAL LADDER, I JOINED THE ARMY."

Before he joined the army he was a used car dealer and health inspector. He had traveled to the United States, where he learned English and got involved in various scams.

Knowing where his political future lay, he became the lover of Mrs. Hanna, who had recommended him to head the National Guard.

NOW I AM READY TO BE PRESIDENT OF NICARAGUA

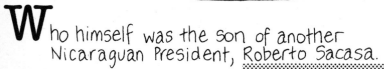

So when the Americans were defeated by Sandino, their interests were well protected with Somoza heading the National Guard.

BUT SANDINO IS STILL ALIVE, DAMN IT!

Somoza and Arthur Bliss Lane, who was the formal United States ambassador, met to discuss the problem presented by a living Sandino...

As a result, on the night of Feb. 21, 1934, the National Guard stopped Sandino and 3 of his aides as they were leaving the National Palace and riddled them with bullets. This was done on the direct orders of Anastasio Somoza, who then saw nothing blocking his path to power.

In the days following the assassination, the National Guard killed over 300 prominent Sandinistas.
This enraged President Sacasa, since all this was going on behind his back.

"SOMOZA DOESN'T KNOW HOW TO APPEAR DEMOCRATIC"

Sacasa tried to control the Guard and oust Somoza, but Somoza moved first.

On June 6, 1936, Sacasa was forced to resign by the Guard, which had besieged the Presidential Palace. He left the country in an American plane and asked for asylum in El Salvador.

NOW IT'S MINE!*

*THE PRESIDENTIAL CHAIR

Elections were soon called to replace the interim president, who was designated by Somoza.

On January 1, 1937 Nicaragua woke up to a new president, who appointed himself Commander of the Guard:

ANASTASIO SOMOZA GARCÍA

Tacho (the Spanish nickname for Anastasio) treated Nicaragua as if it were his personal property.

No business could be transacted without crossing his desk. In twenty years he became owner of everything in Nicaragua: Transportation, Communication, cattle (by 1944 he owned 51 cattle ranches and 46 coffee plantations), land, banks, shops, baseball teams, all kinds of industry, imports of all sorts, customs duties, congressmen...

EVERYTHING!
(associated with the U.S.)

With Somoza in power the United States consolidated its control over Nicaragua...

GOLD, SILVER, COFFEE, COTTON, LUMBER, RUBBER FRUIT: ALL FOR THE U.S.

Somoza controlled all exports, making huge profits on what he sold to the U.S.

TOO BAD WORLD WAR II ENDED!

As a result of supplying the U.S. during World War II Somoza became one of the richest men in Latin America.

He had no opposition. The National Guard took care of anyone who challenged him.

Even though he was a life-long admirer of Hitler and Mussolini, for business reasons Somoza had to declare "war" against fascism.

And he just happened to end up with the property which was confiscated from Germans during the war. Thus he obtained plantations, sugar mills, and import companies without firing a shot.

WE HAVE TO SAVE DEMOCRACY!

GULP

VICTORY IS OURS!

Another of Tacho's scams was gold. Instead of paying taxes, U.S. miners paid Somoza over $400,000 a year.

If cattlemen didn't take their cattle to Somoza's slaughterhouses, the cattle would be confiscated.

At first he was reluctant to share power with the conservative oligarchy. However, in 1948, and again in 1950 to consolidate his power, Somoza signed the Constitutional Pacts, giving the go-ahead to carve up the economy and set the rules of the game.

LET'S SPREAD IT AROUND A LITTLE!

Somoza
would remain
in power with
the labor code
of 1944, which
looked good on
paper, but in reality
meant:

NO
STRIKES,
NO
UNIONS,
NO
TROUBLE-
MAKERS.

The National Guard
pacification plan,
which Somoza
directed,
killed over
20,000 peasants,
workers,
and students,
something
Time-Life
books never
mentioned.

Then one day a worker named Rigoberto López Pérez decided to exchange his life for that of Tacho Somoza García.

Nicaraguans:

Your duty to your country is surpreme
Finish off Somoza in the only way
which he inexorably imposed on you
And which you know so well.

Otherwise,
You will only languish in ignominy
You will not deserve to be a people
But only a herd of cattle.

RIGOBERTO LÓPEZ PÉREZ

Anxiety:

I suffer for my country
In my veins a hero seeks liberation

The flowers of my time will always be
   withered
If the blood of the tyrant is in their veins

I seek the fruit of liberty
in the death of the tyrant.

RIGOBERTO LÓPEZ PÉREZ

León, Nicaragua 1956

The assassination was planned by four Nicaraguans, two of whom were poets.

They were Rigoberto López Pérez, Edwin Castro, Cornelio Silva, and Ausberto Narvaez.

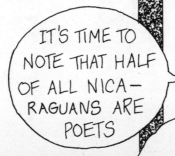

IT'S TIME TO NOTE THAT HALF OF ALL NICA-RAGUANS ARE POETS

83

After dancing a cha cha cha, Rigoberto pumped four bullets into the dictator, who was attending a ball in his honor in León. He was celebrating his umpteenth presidential nomination. It was September 12, 1956.

The U.S. sent a plane to take Tacho to the Canal Zone, but he died anyway

DUELO NACIONAL

29 DE SEPTBRE 1956

PRESIDENTE DE LA ASAMBLEA

2 C   AEREO

NICARAGUA

(as did Rigoberto, riddled on the spot with over 60 bullets).

IT WAS THE BEGINNING OF THE END

However, the death of the tyrant didn't change anything. Even before being shot, Somoza had designated his legitimate sons Luis and Anastasio, Jr., or Tachito, to succeed him. Luis was to be president and Tachito was to be provisional head of the National Guard.

José, an illegitimate son, was a major in the National Guard.

SINCE THEY DIDN'T FLUNK ME AT WEST POINT, DADDY GAVE ME AN ARMY.

In keeping with Tacho's wishes, Luis became president and Tachito took command of the National Guard.

HOW COME THEY SAY LUIS ISN'T REALLY SOMOZA'S SON?

BE- CAUSE HE ACTS LIKE A HUMAN BEING.

Luis Somoza Debayle governed with kid gloves for four years. He freed political prisoners, tolerated some freedom of the press, liberalized the economy a little, and announced that presidents could not be re-elected or pass the position on to their children.

TACHITO WAS FURIOUS!

While Luis was trying to clean up his image, Tachito insisted that everything be done "Somoza–style."

Luis prevailed and imposed René Shick as president. He wasn't even a member of the Somoza tribe . . .

Shick couldn't govern though: Tachito wouldn't let him. So he devoted himself to his favorite pasttime: drinking.

portrait of a dictator
at a young age
Accompanied by his father's sword
and leaning
against the right knee of his whoring mother.

Shick (hic!) died suddenly before his term was over. Tachito designated his good friend Lorenzo Guerrero as interim president.

You guessed it! Anastasio Somoza Debayle was democratically "elected" president of Nicaragua for the 1967-1971 term.

His brother Luis, who opposed Tachito's remaining as head of the National Guard, died suddenly in April 1967. Some say his brother poisoned him.

Junior was left alone to rule Nicaragua just like his Daddy:

IF ANY-BODY DOESN'T LIKE IT, THEY'D BETTER KEEP THEIR MOUTH SHUT.

The traditional opposition in Nicaragua, the conservatives, had been bought off or exiled... and the whole country was parceled out...

OWNERS OF NICARAGUA

SOMOZA GROUP

BANIC GROUP (BANK OF NICARAGUA)

BANAMERICA GROUP (BANK OF AMERICA)

Cotton growing, stores on the Pacific Coast and in Managua (the Guerrero, Montealegré, Reyes, and Montalván families)

The traditional oligarchy, cattle men and merchants, sugar planters and alcohol producers (the Chamorro, Pellas, and Bernad families based in Granada

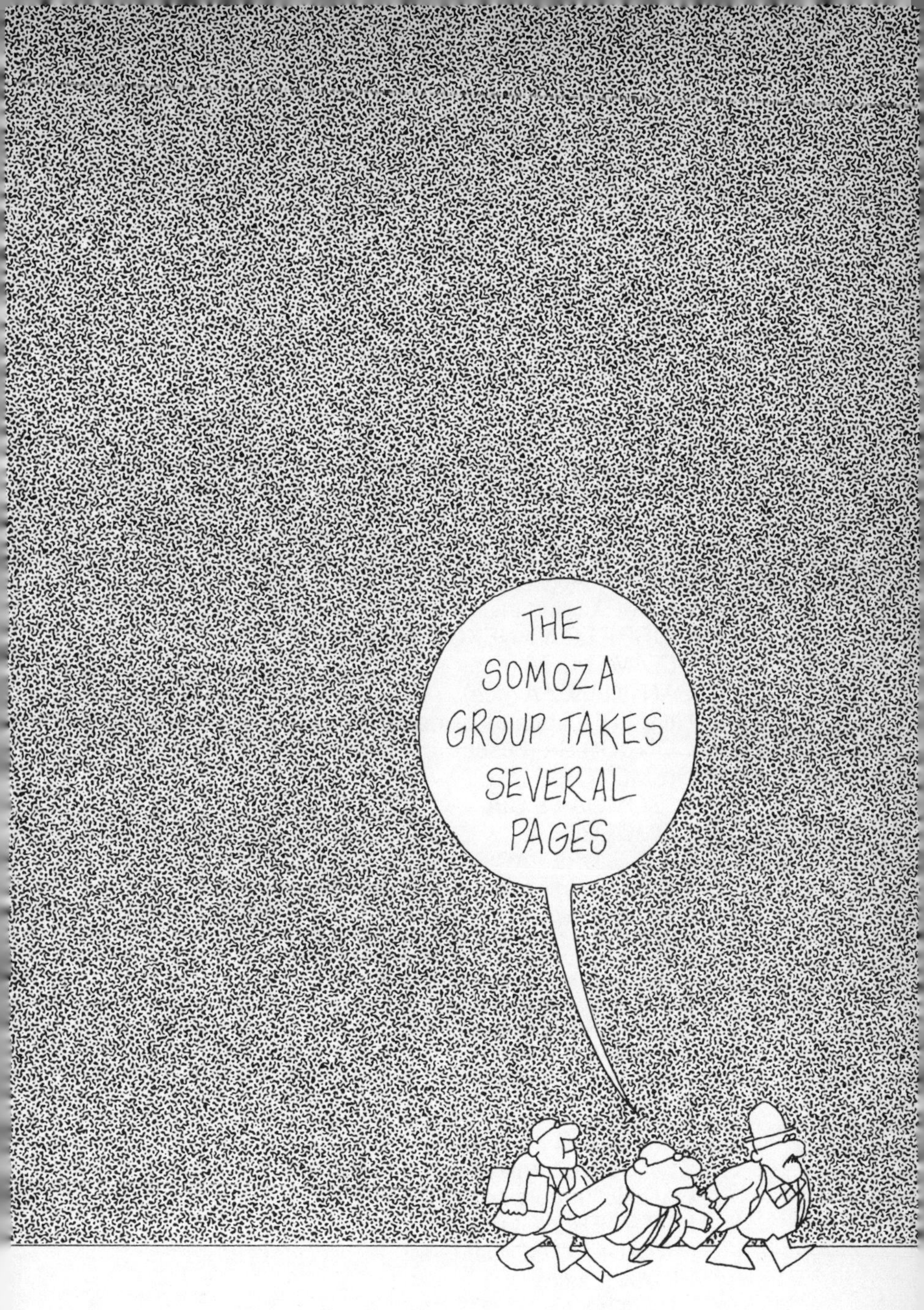
THE SOMOZA GROUP TAKES SEVERAL PAGES

A ROUGH INVENTORY OF THE
SOMOZA FAMILY FORTUNE

ACEITERA CORONA (oils)
AMARNIC (shipping)
Agronica (farm exports)
NIAPSA (Savings and loan bank)
CAPSA (savings and finance)
AISA (construction financing)
INCA (nails and wire)
MONTELIMAR (rum)
AGRICULTURA, Inc. (cotton)
AEROTECNICA, SA. (crop dusting)
CIAS. AGROPECUARIAS, SA (cotton)
INMUEBLES, SA (housing and real estate)
ALMANICA (warehouses)
ALUMEX (aluminium)
MORRILLO Y ANEXOS (rice)
ALTAMIRA, SA (rice)
SAN JUAN, SA (rice)
NICALIT (asbestos cement)
CONDOR SA (buses)
DISMOTOR
A. SOMOZA & CIA ⎤
COMDECOSA ⎬ Cars & Trucks
AUTOS DEL PACIFICO ⎦
LANICA (airline)
10 Sugar mills
CASTLE COOK (bananas)
BANK OF CENTRAL AMERICA
PACSA (fishing boats)
CELTA, SA (lumber)
AGROINCA ⎤
GRANO DE ORO ⎬ Coffee
COMPRABESNIC (shipping)
MAYCO IND., SA (lime)
DORESTA (furniture)
CARNIC (meat packing)
MATADERO IGOSA (slaughterhouse)
MATADERO CONDECA
IFGAN (cattle)
CENTRAL MEAT PACKERS
CELULOSA SUBNARA (cellulose)
EINSA (bottles)
PAPELES Y CARTONES, SA (Paper)
CONAPROCE (cement)
FOSFORERA MOMO TOMBO (matches)

AISLITE (insulation)
ESINCA (roofs)
TANIC
NICARAGUA CIGARS
HACIENDA LA MIA
IND. TABACALERA DEL NORTE — tobacco
HOYOS DE NICARAGUA
VEGAS DE JALAPA
CENTROAM. DE TOBACO
ANITA, SA
PORQUERIZA DEL REGALO (Hams)
TEATROS AGUERRI (cinemas)
OPERADORA DE CINES (cinemas)
DORMICENTRO
F.A. MENDIETA — stores
TELEVISION DE NICARAGUA
TIENDAS ALICIA
CONCRETO PREMEZCLADO (concrete)
PRODUCTOS DE CONCRETO: SA (concrete)
MAYCO INDUSTRIAL (quarries)
Machinery and Construction
PROCISA (data processing)
INTUCSA
CASANICA — construction
PANELFAB
LA CHONTAL (leather)
SONIDO INDUSTRIAL (records, phonographs)
PUERTO LIBRE SA (Duty free shop)
ENERGETICOS SA (energy)
ESINCA (chemicals)
MAMENIC LINE (shipping)
MARTIMA MUNCIAL FERRY, SA
SOSACLORA DE NICARAGUA (chlorine)
REVISTA VISION (a magazine)
INQUISA (fertilizers)
HERCULES DE C.A. (fertilizers)
ELECROQUIMCA PENNSALT (chemicals)
ABONOS SUPERIORES, SA (fertilizers)
63 Cattle ranches
HIELO POLAR (ice)
CIA. LA HIELERA (ice)
HOTELES DE NICARAGUA, SA
HOTEL EL RECREO
HOTELERA IRAZU (in Costa Rica)
GRAN HOTEL (San Salvador)
HOTEL VILLAMAONA (Madrid)
EDITORIAL NOVEDADES (a newspaper)
JOYERIA DREHER (jewelry)
PROLACASA (milk)
CIA, PRODUCT ORA DE LECHE (milk)

LECHA LA COMPLETA (milk)
NESTLÉ ALIMENTANA
HACENDADO UNIDOS, SA
LAVOMATIC (laundry)
MATRA (machinery and transport)
COMERCIAL IBERICA (farm machinery)
INTUCASA (machinery)
TRAKSA (Komatsu tractors)
CIA. AGROPEC OMETEPE (honey)
PRO. FARMAC SOLKA (pharmaceuticals)
METSA (metal and metal buildings)
FISH MEAL CO.
SOLEC FISHERIES
COPESMAP
MARITIMA MUNDIAL ⎤
PROMARBLUE |
BIONICA, SA   ⎬ fishing
PESCANICA, SA |
PESQUERA INTERC. ⎦
9 Publishing companies
PUERTO SOMOZA
PUERTO ISABEL ports
Television de Nic. (TV station)
RADIO EQUIS (Radio Station)
SALINAS NICARAGUENSES (salt)
LA NACIONAL (insurance)
OLORSALINA (soda)
HILADOS Y TEJIDOS EL PORVENIR (cloth)
TEJIDOS CIRCULARES, SA (weaving)
URBANIZAD ORA POLANCO
REPARTO LAS AMERICAS (a subdivision)
URBANIZ. y DESARROLLO (real estate)
ACENCIAS REPRES. NIC (Real estate)
NICARO, S.A. (real estate)
TUBOS DE CENTROAMERICA (pipe)
INICSA (pipe)
ARTURO CUADRA & CIA. (Travel agents)
BROWN & MONTIEL (Travel agents)
VIAJES AMERICANO (Travel agents)
VIAJES UNIVERSOO (Travel agents)
BOUTIQUES LETTY (Travel agents)
and organized smuggling etc.

NO WONDER THEY SAID HE OWNED NIC-ARAGUA!

THANK GOD HE WASN'T INTERESTED IN CHURCH BUSINESS!

Transnational interests in Nicaragua (mostly American) included the following companies:

BRITISH AMERICAN TOBACCO • GENERAL MILLS
NABISCO INC • EXXON • NESTLÉ ALIMENTANA
RALSTON PURINA • SEARS • UNITED FRUIT CO.
QUAKER OATS • ASARCO • WARD FOODS • EVANS PRODUCTS
DRESDNER BANK • BANK OF AMERICA • SINGER
FIRST NATIONAL CITY BANK • LLOYD'S BANK
ST. REGIS PAPER • AMERICAN CYANAMID • SHELL
WESTERN INT. HOTELS • ABBOT LABORATORIES
COLGATE - PALMOLIVE • HOFFMAN LA ROCHE • XEROX
ATLAS CHEMICAL INC. • BORDEN INC • U.S. STEEL
H.B. FULLER CO. • RCA VICTOR • MITSUI SHINETSU
MOHAWK • OLIN CORPORATION • G.T. & E. • MONSANTO
ADELA INVESTMENT • PENNWALT • SHERATON HOTELS
UNITED BRANDS • WINTHROP PLYWOOD • HUGHES TOOLS
WESTINGHOUSE • ETCETERA

Somoza, Jr., was certainly correct in 1974 when he told the Mexican paper Excelsior:

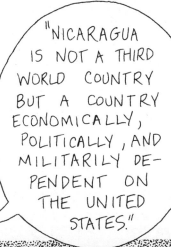

"NICARAGUA IS NOT A THIRD WORLD COUNTRY BUT A COUNTRY ECONOMICALLY, POLITICALLY, AND MILITARILY DEPENDENT ON THE UNITED STATES."

The Somoza family wealth was estimated at $900 million, quite a lot when you consider how poor Nicaragua was.

Despite Somoza's enormous wealth and foreign investment, Nicaragua was one of the poorest countries on earth.

36% unemployment			
74% illiteracy		**73%** substandard housing	
20% children die before age four		**60%** malnutrition	
		80% kids without school	

Chapter 4:

The Children
of Sandino

"our man in Managua"

The American empire, whose marines left in 1933, returned disguised as businessmen, and cut a deal with the Somoza family...

WAS SANDINO'S STRUGGLE IN VAIN?

The struggle against the Somozas began with Rigoberto López Pérez's killing of the old tyrant.

Popular rejoicing was dampened by the fierce repression which Somoza's sons unleashed in search of "accomplices" to the killing. Hundreds of students were imprisoned, including Carlos Fonseca and Tomás Borge.

IT WASN'T HOMICIDE, IT WAS PESTICIDE.

WHO WAS CARLOS FONSECA AMADOR?

He was born in Matagalpa in 1935—the son of a humble cook. As best he could, he attended primary and secondary school and then in 1954 enrolled in Law School in Managua.

In 1955 he joined the Nicaraguan Socialist Party (which was really the Nicaraguan Communist Party) and soon became a student leader, traveling to the 1957 World Youth Festival in Moscow.

In 1958 Carlos participated in an uprising led by the old Sandinista colonel Ramón Raudales, who was killed fighting the National Guard. In 1959 Carlos was training for guerrilla warfare in Honduras when he was seriously wounded by the army. He was captured and deported to Guatemala. He then went to Cuba to recuperate and study how the Cubans got rid of Batista (by this time he had left the party).

The Cuban victory thrilled young Nicaraguans, who decided to repeat the Cuban experience. Between 1958 and 1960 there were over 60 armed uprisings, all of them smashed by the Guard.

GUERRILLA WARFARE SURE BEATS TRIGONOMETRY!

Given their lack of arms, training and organization, the guerrilla groups of the time were easy prey for the Guard, armed and trained by the U.S.

WE'RE THE BEST MILITARY UNIT IN LATIN AMERICA!

Fonseca returned to Nicaragua in 1960 and was jailed. Once he was freed, he began to organize the survivors into one group.

Thus all the nationalists formed one group, the Sandinista movement, later called the National Liberation Front. Finally (in 1963) it adopted the name of **FSLN**＊

＊ in Spanish the initials stand for Sandinista National Liberation Front.

There were ten founders of the FSLN:

Carlos Fonseca
Santos López
Jorge Navarro
Silvio Mayorga
Germán Pomarez
Faustino Ruiz
Tomás Borge
Rigoberto Cruz
Fco. Buitrago &
José Benito Escobar

They adopted Sandino's old black and red flag, as well as the living ideology of the hero of the Segovias.

GET RID OF THE SOMOZAS!

AND OTHER PESTS.

It was quite a challenge: The Guard was strong and the people were de-politicized. In addition, Somoza had the economic, political, and military support of the United States.

The struggle was incredibly hard and long : 18 years! It's almost impossible to summarize this veritable epic of a people willing to die to be free.

1963-1970:

Until 1970 the Front was isolated from the masses. It devoted itself to clandestine organizing, surviving the brutal repression, and gaining enough moral authority to mobilize the people against Somoza.

THE FRONT DID ALL THIS WITH BANK HEISTS, GUERRILLA ATTACKS, SEIZING RADIO STATIONS, AND POLITICAL WORK WITH PEASANTS.

The first
objective of
guerrilla warfare
—SURVIVAL—
was achieved,
though many
compañeros
fell along
the way:

The last two
were killed
in Pancasán,
where the
guerrillas
suffered a
serious defeat.
Twelve of them
were castrated
and killed by
the Guard.

That same year,
1967, a demon-
stration against
Somoza's election
was machine-
gunned, leaving
almost 400
persons dead in
the center of
Managua.

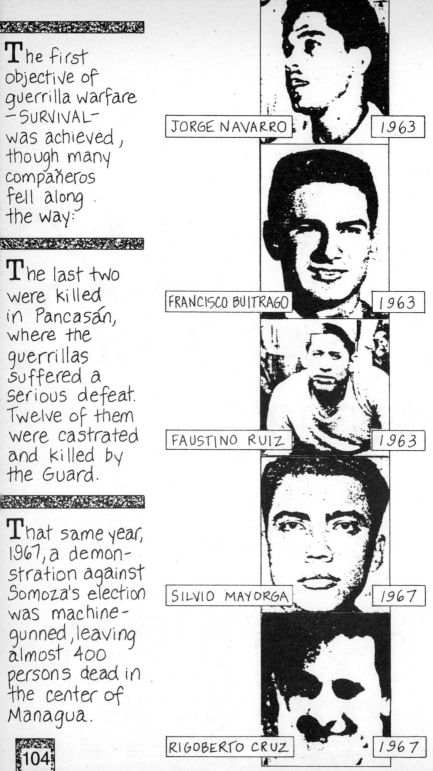

JORGE NAVARRO — 1963

FRANCISCO BUITRAGO — 1963

FAUSTINO RUIZ — 1963

SILVIO MAYORGA — 1967

RIGOBERTO CRUZ — 1967

They weren't the only ones to die. On different occasions the following were killed:

RENÉ CARRIÓN
HUGO MEDINA
FERNANDO GORDILLO
LUCIANO VILCHEZ
EDMUNDO PÉREZ
CASIMIRO SOTELO
ROBERTO AMAYA
AND
SELÍM SHIBLE

In April 1968 two former Guard officers who had joined the FSLN, David and René Tejada, were tortured by Somoza's personal assistant. David died and was thrown into Santiago volcano, which is still active. The whole world was horrified by the cruelty of Somoza, who merrily went about his business as if nothing was happening.

SOMOZA IS A SON OF A BITCH!

YES, BUT HE IS OUR SON OF A BITCH

The
1970 -1974
period was
a difficult time,
during which
the Sandinistas
built up
their strength.

They had to develop their human and material base, set up clandestine schools for combatants, and gather arms and money for the final struggle against Somoza. They survived attempts by the Guard to encircle them in the mountains and organized people in the cities as well. Somoza thought he had finished the FSLN off, but it was alive and well.

SANDINO VIVE

FSLN

MADE IN USA

In December 1972, an earthquake destroyed Managua, causing up to 20,000 deaths!

MY IMAGE SUFFERED A LITTLE...

The main beneficiaries were Somoza, who stole foreign assistance funds sent for quake victims, and the Guard, which looted the rubble that had been Managua.

✳ Especially due to what happened later...

Two guerrilla actions were sufficient to
(a) make Somoza look ridiculous, and
(b) show the world the strength and
seriousness of the Sandinistas.

The first was the take-over of Chema
Castillo's house.

On December 27, 1974 a Sandinista commando group burst into a fancy party in honor of the U.S. ambassador, taking various ambassadors and high officials as hostages. They demanded freedom for political prisoners, $5 million ransom, wage increases for workers, and the publication of statements in newspapers and on the radio. Somoza had to agree to almost everything (although he bargained them down to $2 million ransom).

Nevertheless, 1976 was a difficult year for the Front. Tomás Borge was arrested and tortured, as were 13 other Sandinistas.

And worse, on the 8th of November the founder of the FSLN, Carlos Fonseca Amador, was killed in Zinica.

Somoza asked Uncle Sam for help and soon yankee advisors arrived.

In 1976 and 1977 many "compas" were killed:

IRWING R. URCUYO
FABIO MARTÍNEZ
J. ANTONIO RÍOS
EDGAR MUNGUÍA
ROBERTO HUEMBES
EDUARDO CONTRERAS
SILVIO REÑASCO
ROGELIO PICADO
RUFO MARÍN
CLAUDIA CHAMORRO
WALTER PENTZKE
CARLOS AGUERO
LUZ MARINA SILVA
MARÍA M. AVENDAÑO
ANGELITA MORALES
FELIX PEDRO PICADO

And more guerrillas died:

FSLN

ARLENE SIU
RENÉ TEJADA
HUGO ARÉVALO
MARIO ESTRADA
GILBERTO ROSTRÁN
JULIA H. DE POMARES
MERCEDES REYES
JUAN ESPINOZA
LEÓNIDAS ESPINOZA
JACINTO HERNÁNDEZ
FIDEL AGUILAR
BONIFACIO MONTOYA
TINO MALDONADO
FILEMÓN RIVERA

AUGUSTO SALINAS
JORGE SINFOROSO B.
J. DE DIOS MUÑOZ
RAÚL GONZÁLEZ
ISRAEL LEWITES
ERNESTO MEDRANO
ROBERTO PICHARDO
ELVIS CHAVARRÍA
DONALD GUEVARA
MAX SOMARRIBA
PEDRO ARAUZ
CARLOS ARROYO
GENOVEVA RODRÍGUEZ

With the assassination (ordered by Tacho's son and heir designate: Antonio Somoza, Jr.) of Pedro Joaquín Chamorro, editor of the conservative, anti-Somoza <u>La Prensa</u>, the FSLN's situation improved in 1978.

RESIGN? WHY, I'M IN GOOD HEALTH.

"Los Doce," a group of twelve anti-Somocistas, soon formed. It included priests, intellectuals, and businessmen who demanded the dictator's resignation.

Students throughout the country went on strike, even at Catholic schools.

The right wing formed an opposition party, the Nicaraguan Democratic Movement, led by a businessman named Robelo!

Somoza was shaken.
By this time nobody wanted
him, not even the U.S.

His American wife even left
him, since the dictator was
living with a
prostitute, Dinorah,
to whom he gave
a chain of fancy
boutiques.

Something
was rotten
in the state
of Nicaragua.

On August 22, 1978, a Sandinista commando unit, with a woman as one of its leaders, took the National Palace when Congress was in session, thus forcing Somoza to free Tomás Borge and other political prisoners, pay a half million dollars ransom, and publish Sandinista manifestos.

Somoza was humiliated; even his own newspaper published the Sandinista communiqué.

This set off a popular insurrection, signaling the end of Somoza.

The Nicaraguan people rose up en masse against the Guard in Matagalpa, Chinandega, León, Masaya and Managua.

Everybody was involved: Indians from Monimbó, guerrillas in the mountains, peasants in Jinotega, and old Sandinistas in Wiwilí.

WITH A SINGLE VOICE: PATRIA LIBRE O MORIR!

Once again more than a hundred Nicaraguans who loved their country as much as Sandino came forward.

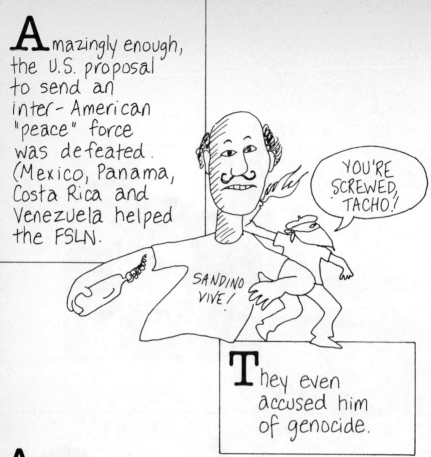

Amazingly enough, the U.S. proposal to send an inter-American "peace" force was defeated. (Mexico, Panama, Costa Rica and Venezuela helped the FSLN.

YOU'RE SCREWED, TACHO!

SANDINO VIVE!

They even accused him of genocide.

And genocide it was!

When Somoza saw he was losing, he ordered the indiscriminate bombing of towns, cities, factories, churches and hospitals. He took all the money he could find (his and the treasury's).

With the defeat of Somoza and the National Guard, de facto killing of kids over the age of 13 took place in the streets, regardless of whether or not they were Sandinistas.

By then nothing could prevent the defeat of the Guard and the U.S. mercenaries. Somoza could only have stayed in power by killing every Nicaraguan.

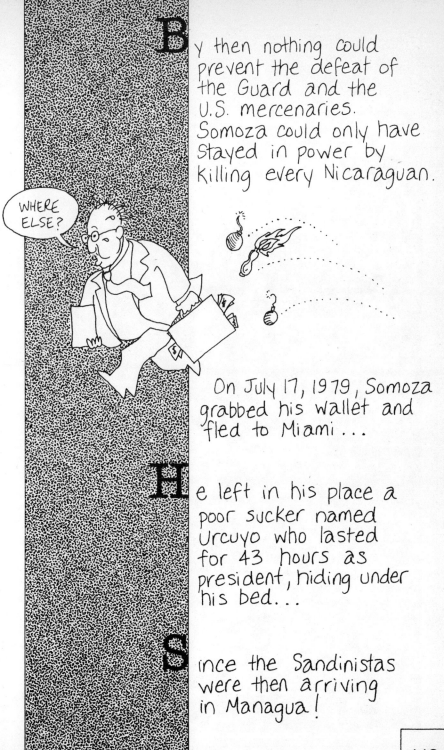

WHERE ELSE?

On July 17, 1979, Somoza grabbed his wallet and fled to Miami...

He left in his place a poor sucker named Urcuyo who lasted for 43 hours as president, hiding under his bed...

Since the Sandinistas were then arriving in Managua!

The victory took a heavy toll. The UN reported:

40,000 dead
200,000 families homeless
40,000 orphans
750,000 without food
1 million refugees

A foreign debt of
$1.6 billion
A third of all
industry destroyed.

Somoza
left a destroyed,
indebted country...

Despite this
the people
were happy!
They had
finally liberated
themselves, not
only from Somoza,
but from the
colonizer
from the North!

ANOTHER CUBA!

A new Cuba?
No, the beginning of a new Nicaragua.

The Sandinista victory and the flight of the Guard brought forth a popular outburst, especially among the poor, who looted stores in Managua...

BELONGING TO SOMOZA'S ACCOMPLICES!

Another act of "justice" was the killing without trial or other formalities of killer cops, informants, torturers and military.

(Only a few were killed: the 300 who didn't manage to escape.)

SOMOZA SAVES

The Sandinistas could do little to stop this explosion of popular wrath by those seeking vengeance for 40 years of abuse and exploitation.

NOW THAT THERE IS NO GOVERNMENT!

Such a response was inevitable in a country which had suffered 40 years of injustice, terror, corruption and oppression.

The people, by destroying everything relating to Somocismo, wanted to start anew: begin a new life, blotting out the old, eliminating everything which hadn't been destroyed by the war and the earthquake.

Once the nightmare of Somocismo was over, the reconstruction had to begin; that is, a revolution.

127

Now there will be another war and another struggle. The struggle against the backwardness and poverty, the struggle against ignorance, the struggle to instill in every revolutionary heart a love for the people.

Tomás Borge, only surviving founder of the FSLN.

"This revolution is irreversible, and not only that, this revolution will be carried to its ultimate consequences. Not surprisingly, there are some people who don't like that, who ask us where we are going. They say it's dangerous, that this revolution is communist. We say no, this revolution is not communist, it is a Sandinista revolution.

"But we could say this revolution is communist and not take revolutionary measures, and the enemies of our people would be happy. It is not names, but acts that count. Labels don't make revolutions, action does!"

THESE REVOLUTIONARIES SURE AREN'T LIKE MEXICAN REVOLUTIONARIES!

AND WHY A "NEW" NICARAGUA???

BECAUSE THE OLD ONE WAS NEVER OURS.

Occupied by the U.S. from 1912 to 1933, and from 1933 to 1979 by Somoza, a servant of the U.S., Nicaragua has never been able to use its wealth to help its people. (It went from being a Spanish colony to being a U.S. colony.

SOMOZA BORROWED MONEY TO BUY GUNS

TO KILL HIS OWN PEOPLE!

SANDINO VIVE!

When victory came, each Nicaraguan's share of the foreign debt was $600 ... money which they had never seen, but which had to be repaid ... And where was the money to rebuild the country?

HE LEFT ONLY $3.5 MILLION DOLLARS IN THE TREASURY. PEANUTS.

One of the first steps taken by the Junta of National Reconstruction was the confiscation and nationalization of all the property of Somoza and his accomplices (which has already been listed) and 1.2 million acres of land.

WOW, HALF OF THE CULTIVATABLE LAND IN THE COUNTRY!

500 houses of Somocistas who fled were expropriated and used as day care centers, old age homes, health centers and schools.

Banks were nationalized.

AS WERE ALL NATURAL RESOURCES (ESPECIALLY THE MINES)

Creating a new Nicaraguan was even more important than creating a new Nicaragua.

The people were given what Somoza had systematically denied them.

°50.2 % of Nicaraguans are illiterate.

°70 % of Nicaraguans don't have medical attention.

°20 % of all children die before reaching the age of four.

ABC

Over 100,000 young people participated in the literacy campaign.
In ten months they not only ended illiteracy, but they put city kids in touch with the reality of rural Nicaragua.

I THOUGHT YOU PEASANTS WERE LIKE THE GUYS ON "BONANZA."

NATIONAL LITERACY CAMPAIGN:"HEROES AND MARTYRS OF NICARAGUAN LIBERATION."

A little anecdote: On September 17, 1980 an
Argentine Montonero commando unit
liquidated don Anastasio Somoza in
Asunción, Paraguay. He was 53.
You reap what you sow.

For a people depoliticized after 40 years of Somocismo and anti-communism, the literacy campaign was an important factor in uniting the country and incorporating people into the revolution.

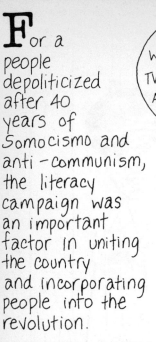

DON'T FORGET, WE'VE BEEN PRACTICALLY TWO COUNTRIES, THE ATLANTIC AND PACIFIC.

The Atlantic Coast is home to another race, with its own language, religion and culture. It only found out it was part of Nicaragua when thousands of teachers, sociologists, doctors and literacy workers arrived from the "other" Nicaragua.

HERE COME THOSE GUYS WHO KEEP CALLING ME "BROTHER" AND "COMPAÑERO".

THEY MUST WANT TO SELL YOU SOMETHING.

For the first time in their life the inhabitants of the Atlantic Coast participated in something which affected them directly. Literacy began to change their lives and health programs made even bigger changes . . .

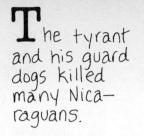

The tyrant and his guard dogs killed many Nicaraguans.

FORTUNATELY SOMOZA IS NOW IN THE TRASH-BIN OF HISTORY!

BUT THERE'S STILL ONE KILLER LOOSE!

AS BAD AS THE GUARD?

In the corrupt system which existed before, money which should have been used to build hospitals was stolen.

How many hospitals, of the few there were, did Somoza destroy before fleeing?

Indeed, getting rid of Somocismo also got rid of corruption, since it is the sine qua non of capitalism...

But you can't shoot malnutrition and filth.

> AND YOU CAN'T END DISEASE WITH A DECREE!

Nor with 8,000 hospitals and 500 Health Departments.

In the past, Nicaragua had 22 health institutions which openly competed to see who could steal the most and "help" the most sick people.

> TO END ALL THIS CONFUSION, THE SANDINISTA REVOLUTION CREATED A SINGLE HEALTH CARE SYSTEM.

Medicine was just another business, and the principal goal of those who "cared" for the sick was to convert people into a source of income.

> THE MORE SICK PEOPLE THERE ARE, THE MORE MONEY YOU MAKE.

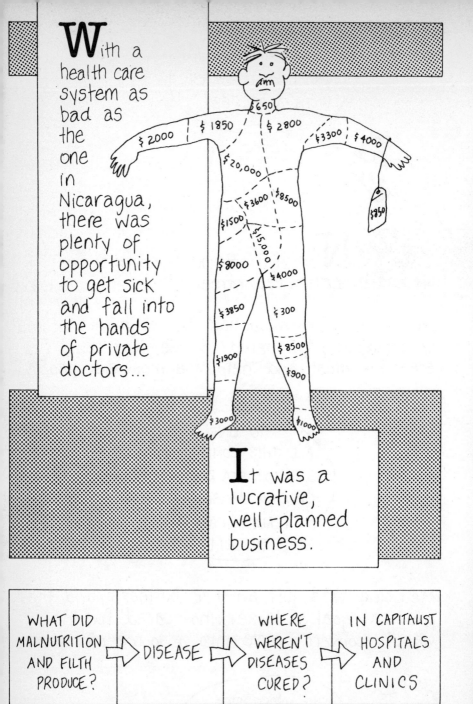

With a health care system as bad as the one in Nicaragua, there was plenty of opportunity to get sick and fall into the hands of private doctors...

It was a lucrative, well-planned business.

WHAT DID MALNUTRITION AND FILTH PRODUCE? ⇒ DISEASE ⇒ WHERE WEREN'T DISEASES CURED? ⇒ IN CAPITALIST HOSPITALS AND CLINICS

How can you have private medicine without sick people?

Medicine under capitalism is organized as a business: If you don't have any sick people, you don't have any profits...

And without the poor people, there would be no ladies of St. Vincent, nor charity hospitals, nor filthy rich doctors nor millionaire health officials with five luxury cars at the side of their expensive homes...

...nor another important business in Latin America...

MULTI-NATIONAL PHARMACEUTICAL COMPANIES

IF THERE ARE NO SICK PEOPLE, WHO CAN WE SELL OUR DRUGS TO?

GOOD HEALTH ISN'T A RESULT OF THE NUMBER OF DOCTORS, HOSPITALS, PHARMACIES AND PHARMACEUTICAL COMPANIES...

Where does it come from then?

PEOPLE ARE HEALTHY WHEN THEY THEMSELVES TAKE PART IN HEALTH CARE!

AND YOU HAVE TO GET PEOPLE ORGANIZED BEFORE IT WILL WORK.

Ever since the insurrection began, Nicaraguans have been organizing themselves. After the triumph, mass organizations were created, more or less following the Cuban model. Neighborhood committees on each block, groups in work centers, women's groups, Sandinista youth, trade unions, small land-owners, teachers, students, health-care workers, agricultural workers, everybody.

CDS

fetSaLUD

anden

APF

ATC

ANS

AMNLAE

JS.19J.

From the mass organizations emerged the People's Health Commission to coordinate all these efforts with the Health Ministry.

CST

145

...An example:

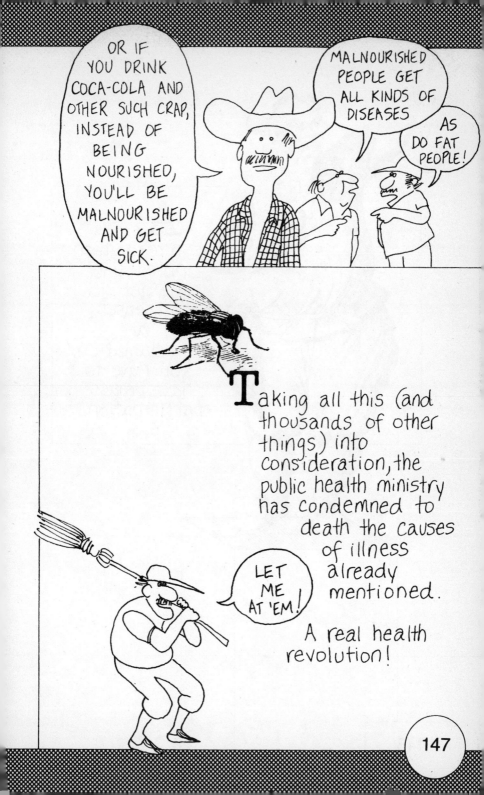

OR IF YOU DRINK COCA-COLA AND OTHER SUCH CRAP, INSTEAD OF BEING NOURISHED, YOU'LL BE MALNOURISHED AND GET SICK.

MALNOURISHED PEOPLE GET ALL KINDS OF DISEASES

AS DO FAT PEOPLE!

Taking all this (and thousands of other things) into consideration, the public health ministry has condemned to death the causes of illness already mentioned.

A real health revolution!

LET ME AT 'EM!

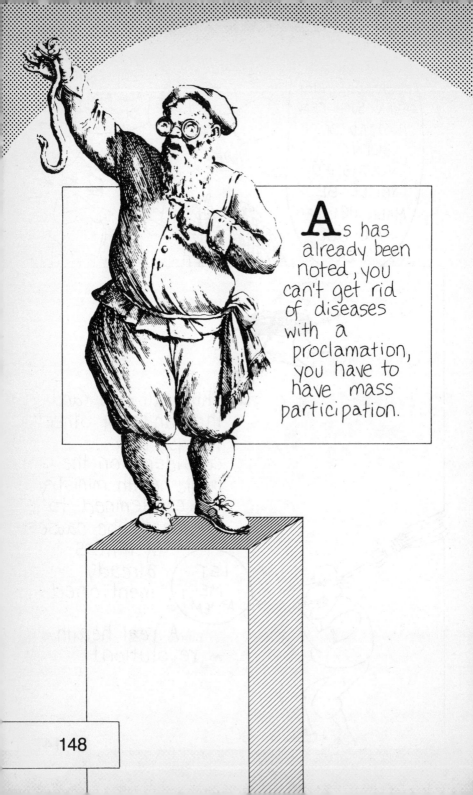

As has already been noted, you can't get rid of diseases with a proclamation, you have to have mass participation.

148

Thus after the literacy campaign a program began to educate people about health, through vaccination programs, clean-ups, nutrition seminars, and discussions about public health.

Public Health campaigns (in which almost everyone participates) are a major Sandinista victory in the effort to integrate the people into the revolution.

THE HEALTH AND LITERACY CAMPAIGNS ARE ONLY TWO OF THE THINGS THE REVOLUTION HAS DONE TO INTEGRATE THE PEOPLE INTO THE REVOLUTIONARY PROCESS AND GET THEM TO PARTICIPATE

Other accomplishments have been the creation of militias to defend the country against American aggression.

Changing relations between workers and bosses, and reforms in education, culture, and in mass communication.

CREATING PRODUCERS' CO-OPS...

THAT IS TO SAY, NICARAGUA IS HEADED TOWARD ATHEIST SOCIALISM?

And
what
does
the
Nicaraguan
church
say?

In a pastoral letter of the Nicaraguan Episcopals dated November 17, 1979, the bishops stated:

"At times one hears expressed with anguish the fear that the present Nicaraguan revolutionary process is leading to socialism. If, as some feel, socialism will go astray, depriving men and peoples of their role as a protagonist in their history, if it blindly submits people to the manipulations and the dictates of those who arbitrarily wield power, then we cannot accept this false socialism. Nor can we accept a socialism which, going beyond its legitimate bounds, deprives men of the right to religious belief and the public expression of these beliefs. It is equally unacceptable to deny parents the right to educate their children according to their convictions, or to deny them any other human right. If, however, socialism means, as it should mean, the pre-eminence of the interests of the majority and a nationally planned economy, with mass participation, then we have nothing against which to object.

"In addition, we are confident that the revolutionary process will be something original, profoundly nationalistic and not imitative of other models. What we want, along with the majority of Nicaraguans, is a process which leads to a truly Nicaraguan society; not capitalist, not dependent, not totalitarian."

—Signed by the seven Nicaraguan bishops.

CUERNAVACA, MEXICO   JUNE 1982

NICARAGUA BIBLIOGRAPHY

Arias, Pilar

Nicaragua, Revolución: Relatos de Combatientes del Frente Sandinista. Mexico City, Siglo XXI, 1980.

Black, George

Triumph of the People: The Sandinista Revolution in Nicaragua. London, Zed Press, 1981.

Booth, John A.

The End and the Beginning: The Nicaraguan Revolution. Boulder, Colorado, Westview Press, 1981.

Borge, Tomás, et al.

Sandinistas Speak. New York, Pathfinder Press, 1982.

Collins, Joseph, with Frances Moore Lappé and Nick Allen

What Difference Could a Revolution Make? Food and Farming in the New Nicaragua. San Francisco, Institute for Food and Development Policy, 1982.

Diederich, Bernard

Somoza and the Legacy of U.S. Involvement in Central America. New York, Dutton, 1981.

EPICA Task Force

Nicaragua, A People's Revolution. Washington DC, EPICA, 1980.

Lappé, Frances Moore and Joseph Collins

Now We Can Speak: A Journey through the New Nicaragua. San Francisco, IFDP, 1982.

Meiselas, Susan

Nicaragua (photographs). New York, Pantheon, 1981.

Millett, Richard

Guardians of the Dynasty: History of the U.S.-created Guardia Nacional of Nicaragua and the Somoza Family. New York, Orbis Books, 1977.

Ortega, Humberto   50 Años de Lucha Sandinista.
Havana, Casa de las Américas, 1980.

Ramírez, Sergio   El pensamiento Vivo de Sandino.
San José, Costa Rica, EDUCA, 1977.

Randall, Margaret   Sandino's Daughters: Testimonies
of Nicaraguan Women in Struggle.
Vancouver, New Star Books, 1981.

Rossett, Peter and   The Nicaragua Reader: Documents of
John Vandermeer, eds.   a Revolution Under Fire.
New York, Grove Press, 1983.

Selser, Gregorio   Sandino.
New York, Monthly Review Press, 1981.

Walker, Thomas W.   Nicaragua: The Land of Sandino.
Boulder, Westview Press, 1981.

Walker, Thomas W., ed.   Nicaragua in Revolution.
New York, Praeger, 1982.

Weber, Henri   Nicaragua: The Sandinist Revolution.
Translated by Patrick Camiller.
London, Verso Editions and NCB, 1981.